animate

BIBLE

ILLUSTRATED BY
PAUL SOUPISET

WRITTEN BY
CARLA BARNHILL
& TONY JONES

SPARK
HOUSE
wearesparkhouse.org

| MINNEAPOLIS, MN

CONTRIBUTORS
NADIA BOLZ-WEBER, JAY BAKKER,
ERIC ELNES, RACHEL HELD EVANS,
JOSÉ MORALES, PHYLLIS TICKLE,
WILL WILLIMON

JOURNAL ILLUSTRATION
BY PAUL SOUPISET, WITH ADDITIONAL
ILLUSTRATION BY JULIANA HERNANDEZ,
FOR TOOLBOX STUDIOS, INC.

JOURNAL WRITERS
CARLA BARNHILL, TONY JONES

SPARKHOUSE TEAM
ANDREW DEYOUNG, TONY JONES,
TIMOTHY PAULSON, KRISTOFER SKRADE

TOOLBOX STUDIOS TEAM
PAUL SOUPISET, STACY THOMAS,
SARAH WOOLSEY, JULIANA HERNANDEZ

VIDEO TEAM
KYLE ISENHOWER OF ISENHOWER
PRODUCTIONS, SHANE NELSON OF
OMNI-FUSION MEDIA PRODUCTION,
SILAS KINDY OF ONE LIGHT COLLECTIVE

EDITORIAL TEAM
ERIN DAVIS

SPECIAL THANKS TO PHOTOGRAPHER
COURTNEY PERRY

THE PAPER USED IN THIS PUBLICATION
MEETS THE MINIMUM REQUIREMENTS
OF AMERICAN NATIONAL STANDARD FOR
INFORMATION SCIENCES — PERMANENCE OF
PAPER FOR PRINTED LIBRARY MATERIALS,
ANSI Z329 . 48 -1984

MANUFACTURED IN THE U.S.A.

16 15 14 13 1 2 3 4 5 6 7 8 9 10

ISBN 978-1-4514-7288-2

animate
BIBLE

CANON | MINING FOR THE WORD
ERIC ELNES | 7

HISTORY | PARCHMENT TO PIXEL
PHYLLIS TICKLE | 23

TESTAMENTS | ONE STORY, TWO PARTS
RACHEL HELD EVANS | 39

GOSPELS | UNEXPECTED GOOD NEWS
NADIA BOLZ-WEBER | 55

GENRE | RHYTHM OF THE TEXT
JOSÉ MORALES | 71

INTERPRETATION | SCRIPTURE READS US
WILL WILLIMON | 87

GRACE | LOVE IS THE BOTTOM LINE
JAY BAKKER | 103

This journal is pretty amazing to look at. It's got gorgeous illustrations created by phenomenally talented artists and thought-provoking words from some of the most innovative Christian thinkers and practitioners in the country.

But it's not done, not by a long shot.

The pages of this journal aren't meant to sit there and look pretty. They are intended to be a springboard for your images, your words, your phenomenal creations and thought-provoking ideas. So scribble on the pages, write down your thoughts, color outside of the lines—seriously. Make this thing your own. No one is going to look over your shoulder to check your work. No one is handing out gold stars to the student who gets the right answers. Really, no one is convinced there are right answers.

In a time when the Bible is used in religious, political, and social debates, it seems increasingly important that those of us who claim a faith rooted in this sacred text have a sense of the challenges the Bible presents. The Animate:Bible series was developed as a way of shedding some light on the way Christians think about and use the Bible. It looks into the questions we all have about Scripture:

How did the Bible come to be?

Who chose the books of the Bible?

How should we interpret the Bible?

How do the Old and New Testaments fit together?

Should we read all of the Bible the same way?

What's going on in the Gospels?

Is the Bible even relevant?

 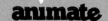

Maybe you've been asking these questions for a while. Maybe you've never really thought much about them. Maybe you've got friends who've been wounded by the Bible. Maybe you've had your own struggle with making sense of the sometimes-strange and violent stories we find in Scripture. Whatever your experience, you're invited to join in a kind of expedition where the route is a little uncharted and the territory a bit mysterious.

If that feels unsettling to you, don't worry. Your fellow travelers are people who've been walking this path for a while—people like Will Willimon and Rachel Held Evans and Jay Bakker and Phyllis Tickle. Each of them is far more interested in asking questions than answering them. So feel free to do the same.

As you work through each session, remember that you are encouraged to speak up when you think the trail is veering off. If something strikes you as worth talking about, talk about it. If something else feels uninspiring, go ahead and skip that part. This is your journey and you get to decide when to stop and linger and when to keep moving.

Along the way, you'll be keeping this journal, creating a kind of keepsake of your travels. During the group sessions, your facilitator will offer suggestions for activities and deeper discussion. But in the days between sessions,

you're encouraged to revisit those ideas that are compelling to you and dig a little more. Add an illustration, write down a question, sketch out an idea, craft a better metaphor.

We hope you end each session with some ink on your fingers. The beautiful pages of this journal aren't meant to stay pristine. They are a springboard meant to plunge you into your own imagination. So doodle, write notes, add your thoughts and questions. Mess with the ideas and the images and see where the conversation takes you.

In the days between sessions, we invite you to join in the growing Animate community. We've put together a host of social media platforms you can use to share your experiences, connect with the creators of Animate: Bible, and hear from other churches and groups using this series around the country. Connect with us on Facebook, Twitter, and Pinterest and tell us what you're thinking:

FACEBOOK.COM/ANIMATESERIES

TWITTER.COM/SHANIMATE

PINTEREST.COM/WEARESPARKHOUSE

We can't wait to find out where Animate takes you!

animate

CANON | MINING FOR THE WORD
ERIC ELNES

eric Elnes

"OUR ANCIENT FOREBEARERS VIEWED THE BOOKS OF SCRIPTURE MORE LIKE ROCKS WITH VEINS OF GOLD RUNNING THROUGH THEM THAN PURE GOLD ITSELF."

Eric Elnes has a PhD in Biblical Studies from Princeton. He is the pastor of Countryside Community Church (UCC) in Omaha, and the host of a weekly webcast called Darkwood Brew.

GOLD!

ASSAY OFFC

Eric suggests that in many ways, the process of canonization is ongoing, that we are also to be looking for the vein of gold that runs through Scripture. How does that idea sit with you?

"The Old Testament God is the creator of evils, lustful for war, inconstant in his attitude, and self-contradictory."

MARCION

ORTHODOXY

HERESY

animate

"No, the God of the Old Testament is the merciful father of Jesus."

Eric offers three guidelines that helped shape the canon and suggests that we continue to ask these questions as we search for "gold" in the Bible.

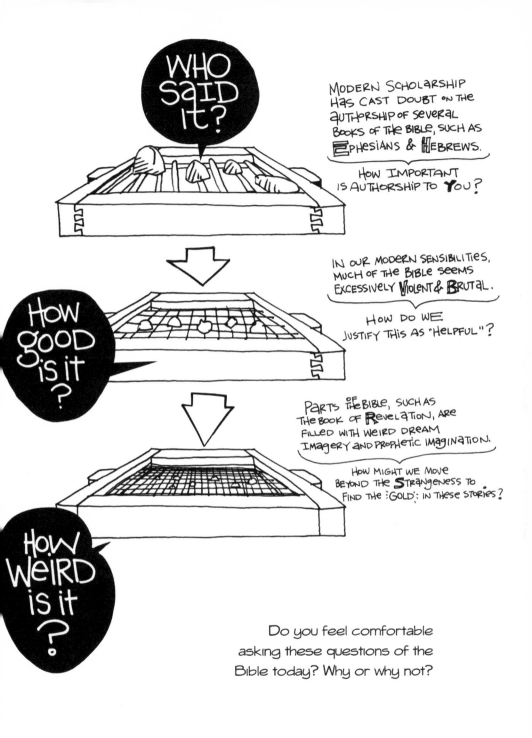

MODERN SCHOLARSHIP HAS CAST DOUBT ON THE AUTHORSHIP OF SEVERAL BOOKS OF THE BIBLE, SUCH AS **E**PHESIANS & **H**EBREWS.

HOW IMPORTANT IS AUTHORSHIP TO **Y**OU?

IN OUR MODERN SENSIBILITIES, MUCH OF THE BIBLE SEEMS EXCESSIVELY **V**IOLENT & **B**RUTAL.

HOW DO WE JUSTIFY THIS AS "HELPFUL"?

PARTS OF THE BIBLE, SUCH AS THE BOOK OF **R**EVELATION, ARE FILLED WITH WEIRD DREAM IMAGERY AND PROPHETIC IMAGINATION.

HOW MIGHT WE MOVE BEYOND THE **S**TRANGENESS TO FIND THE GOLD IN THESE STORIES?

Do you feel comfortable asking these questions of the Bible today? Why or why not?

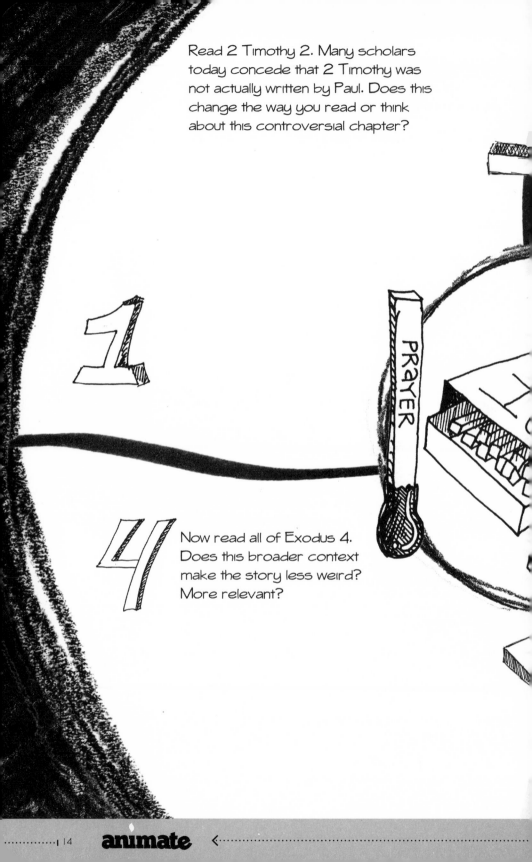

Read 2 Timothy 2. Many scholars today concede that 2 Timothy was not actually written by Paul. Does this change the way you read or think about this controversial chapter?

1

PRAYER

4 Now read all of Exodus 4. Does this broader context make the story less weird? More relevant?

Skim through Chronicles 5 and read Matthew 5. In what ways are these passages helpful or not? How do you determine if something in the Bible is helpful?

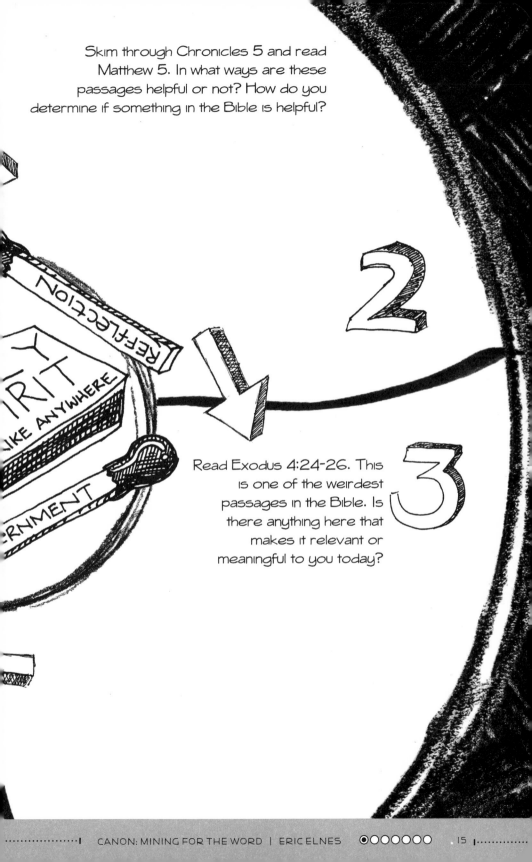

2

REFLECTION

Y
IRIT
IKE ANYWHERE

RNMENT

3

Read Exodus 4:24-26. This is one of the weirdest passages in the Bible. Is there anything here that makes it relevant or meaningful to you today?

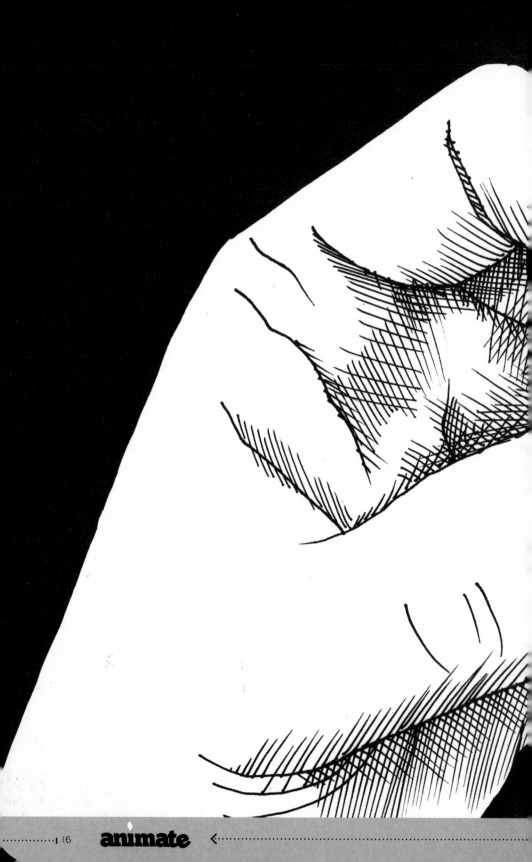

animate

"THOSE WHO CREATED THE CANON MINED THE GOLD FOR US. NOW IT'S OUR JOB TO REFINE THAT GOLD.

ARE YOU READY TO FORGE SOMETHING PRECIOUS OUT OF WHAT WE'VE BEEN GIVEN?"

Notes

WANT MORE? HERE ARE A FEW SUGGESTIONS
FOR FURTHER READING ON THIS TOPIC.

*Constantine's Bible: Politics and the Making of the New
Testament,* David L. Dungan. Fortress Press, 2006.

*How the Books of the New Testament Were
Chosen,* Roy Hoover (Bible Review 9, April
1993), pp. 44-47. http://bit.ly/12oGIoE

Whose Bible Is It? A Short History of the Scriptures,
Jaraslov Pelikan, Penguin, Reprint 2006.

The Bible: A Biography, Karen Armstrong.
Grove Press, 2008.

NOTES

animate

animate

HISTORY | PARCHMENT TO PIXEL
PHYLLIS TICKLE

PHYLLIS TICKLE

Phyllis Tickle is the Grande Dame of American Protestantism. She is the founding editor of the religion department at *Publishers Weekly* and best known for compiling the *Divine Hours*™ prayer books.

"We've gotten comfortable with our access to the Bible."

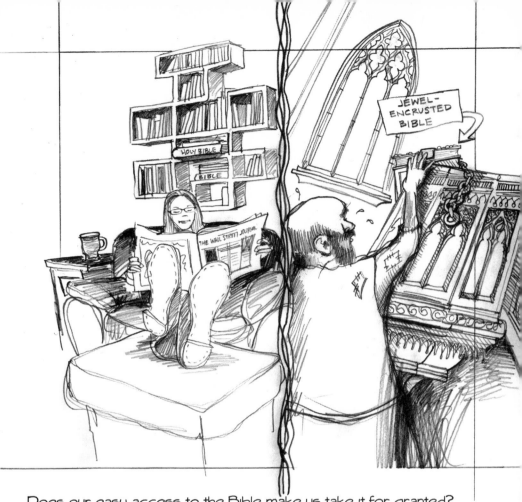

Does our easy access to the Bible make us take it for granted?

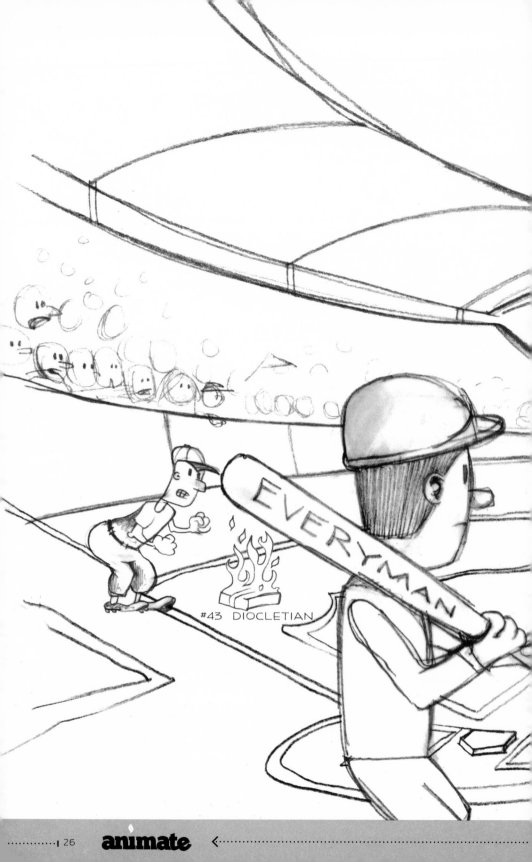

Throughout history, control of the Bible has changed hands dozens of times. Where do you think it's the most safe: in the hands of the "pros" or the hands of the crowd?

#16 TERTULLIAN

#8 GNOSTIC

#34 M. LUTHER

What does each of these forms communicate about the Bible and what it's for?

2 Ask someone to read Jeremiah 33:10-11 without any inflection. Then ask someone to read it with some dramatic flair. Does the more dramatic reading add anything to the text?

1 Read Exodus 25:10-22: What does this passage tell us about the way the ancient Jews viewed God's Word?

4 Outside of reading the Bible or hearing it read in church, in what other places or media have you encountered the Bible? How did those experiences differ from reading the Bible from the page?

3

Read Hebrews 4:12: What does this passage tell us about the role of the Bible in the lives of early Christians? What does it have to say to today's Christians?

What do we gain from our easy access to the Bible? What do we lose?

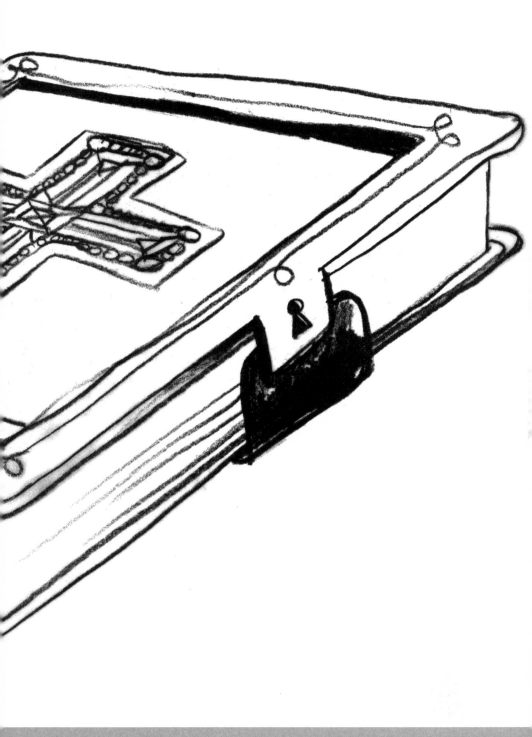

Think about the Bible
something they've learned
role in their Daily life

WANT MORE? HERE ARE A FEW SUGGESTIONS
FOR FURTHER READING ON THIS TOPIC.

*Whose Bible Is It? A History of the Scripture Through
the Ages,* Jaroslav Pelikan, Viking Press, 2005.

*The Reformation of the Bible/The Bible of the
Reformation,* Jaroslav Pelikan with Valerie R. Hotchkiss
and David Price. Yale University Press, 1996.

The Bible in English: Its History and Influence,
David Daniell. Yale University Press, 2003.

Reading the Bible After Christendom, Lloyd
Pietersen. Herald Press, 2012.

Free for All: Rediscovering the Bible in Community,
Tim Conder and Daniel Rhodes. Baker, 2009.

notes

Notes

animate

TESTAMENTS | ONE STORY, TWO PARTS
RACHEL HELD EVANS

RACHEL Held-Evans

Rachel Held Evans is a popular author and blogger. Her most recent book, *A Year of Biblical Womanhood*, is a New York Times bestseller.

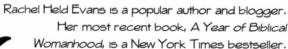

"AS IT TURNS OUT, THESE BIBLE STORIES ARE NOT HAPPY, FEEL-GOOD FAIRY-TALES. NO, THEY ARE MUCH DARKER THAN THAT."

Have you ever been surprised to discover the "Not-Safe-for-Sunday-School" details of a story from the Bible?

What stories from the
Old Testament don't
sit well with you?

What parts of the
Old Testament are
meaningful to you?

animate

How have you made sense of the tension
between the Old Testament and the New Testament?

fairy taLes are NOT Because they teLL but Because they DRAGONS CAN

Rachel suggests that God's love is a thread throughout the Old Testament, even in the midst of the dark and violent stories. How can this idea give us hope in the midst of the darkness and violence in our time?

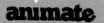

more than true;

us that dragons exist,

tell us that

be beaten.

— G.K. CHESTERTON
(According to Neil Gaiman)

What are your personal dragons
that need to be defeated?
What about the dragons in our world?
When have you seen dragons defeated?

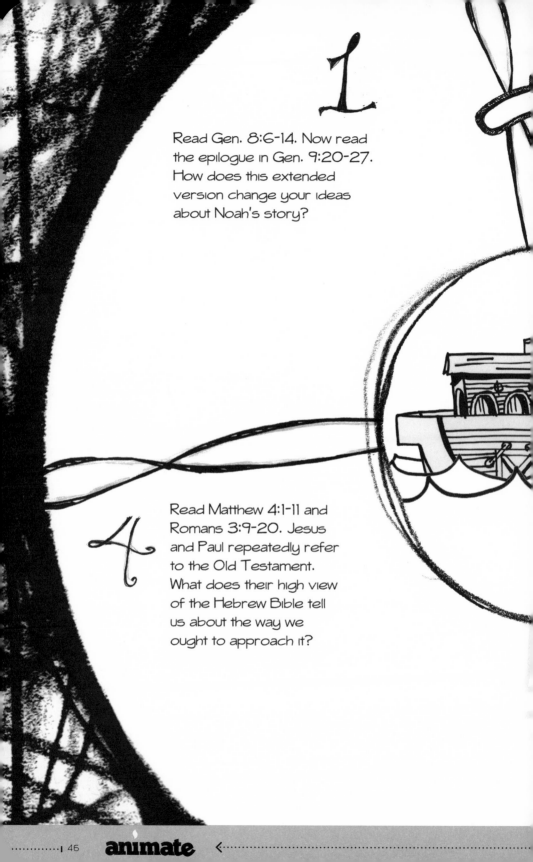

1.

Read Gen. 8:6-14. Now read the epilogue in Gen. 9:20-27. How does this extended version change your ideas about Noah's story?

4.

Read Matthew 4:1-11 and Romans 3:9-20. Jesus and Paul repeatedly refer to the Old Testament. What does their high view of the Hebrew Bible tell us about the way we ought to approach it?

Read 1 Kings 6:3, Lev. 21:17-20, and Ezekiel 5:1-2. Passages like these aren't exactly memory verses. So what do you think we're supposed to make of them?

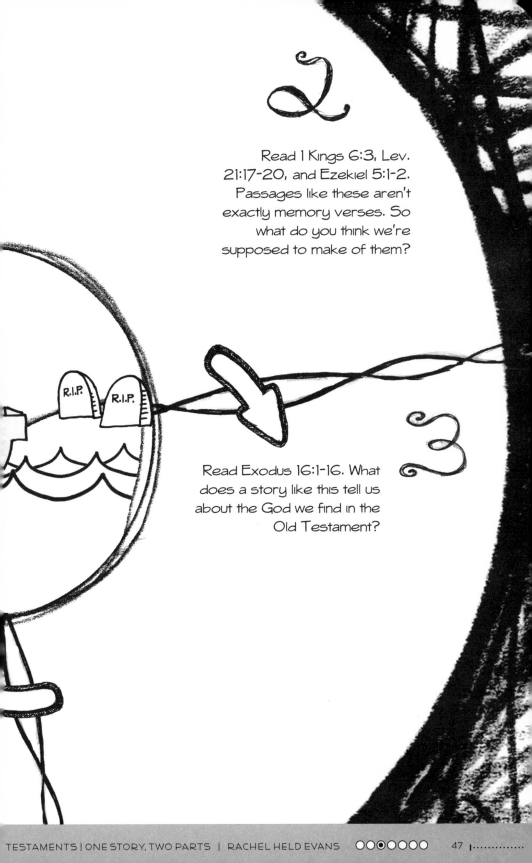

Read Exodus 16:1-16. What does a story like this tell us about the God we find in the Old Testament?

Listen for the
Wisper of love
This week

NOTES

WANT MORE? HERE ARE A FEW SUGGESTIONS
FOR FURTHER READING ON THIS TOPIC.

*Inspiration and Incarnation: Evangelicals and the Problem of
the Old Testament*, Peter Enns. Baker Academic, 2005.

*Eat This Book: A Conversation in the Art of Spiritual
Reading*, Eugene Peterson. Wm. B. Eerdmans, 2009.

*The Blue Parakeet: Rethinking How You Read the
Bible*, Scot McKnight. Zondervan, 2008.

notes

GOSPELS | UNEXPECTED GOOD NEWS
NADIA BOLZ-WEBER

Nadia Bolz-Weber

Nadia Bolz-Weber is the
founding pastor of House
For All Sinners and Saints,
an ELCA mission church
in Denver, Colorado.
Her most recent book
is a theological memoir.

The fact is that anything I would come up with as "Good news" would be hopelessly selfish. That's exactly why I need the Gospel of Jesus Christ and not the Gospel of Nadia. I need a story and an identity and a symbol system and some Good News that comes from a source that is not myself.

NEWS FLASH > WILD MAN BAPTIZING PEOPLE

Nadia mentions some of the ways we use the word "gospel."
What does the word mean to to you?

Good news :>
Truth

Have you ever been
surprised by good news
from an unexpected source?

The beginning
of the
Gospel
of
Jesus
Christ
Son
of
God

The Greek word that we translate as "gospel" is euangelion (εὐαγγέλιον). It has a long history that pre-dates the New Testament. Homer used it as early as the 8th century BC in the Odyssey. Other ancient writers including Aristides, Xenophon, and Plutarch use euangelion as a proclamation of good news. In each case, gospel refers to good news that's proclaimed in a public forum.

CLEVER DISGUISE

EVEN OLD ODYSSEUS uses εὐαγγέλιον!

DRINKS ARE ON THE HOUSE!!

YEAH!

NEWS FLASH FREE BEER AT DOME

animate

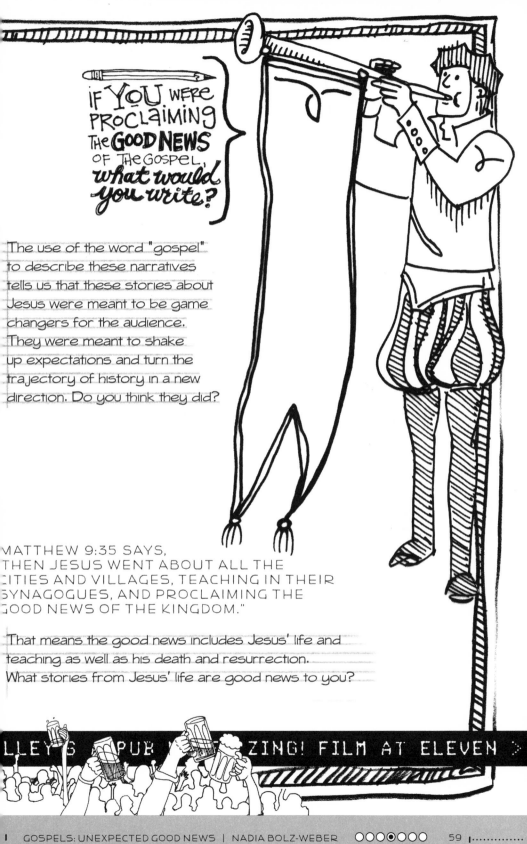

IF YOU WERE PROCLAIMING THE **GOOD NEWS** OF THE GOSPEL, *what would you write?*

The use of the word "gospel" to describe these narratives tells us that these stories about Jesus were meant to be game changers for the audience. They were meant to shake up expectations and turn the trajectory of history in a new direction. Do you think they did?

MATTHEW 9:35 SAYS, "THEN JESUS WENT ABOUT ALL THE CITIES AND VILLAGES, TEACHING IN THEIR SYNAGOGUES, AND PROCLAIMING THE GOOD NEWS OF THE KINGDOM."

That means the good news includes Jesus' life and teaching as well as his death and resurrection. What stories from Jesus' life are good news to you?

LLEY'S PUB ZING! FILM AT ELEVEN

The four Gospels tell four different stories. Matthew, Mark, and Luke share some comm
themes, but John reads like something entirely different.

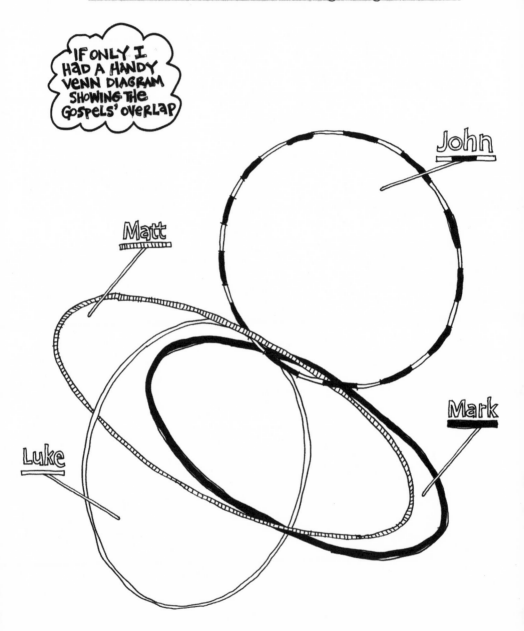

Synoptics

Matthew	Mark	Luke	John
SERMON ON THE MOUNT™	NO SERMON ON THE MOUNT	SERMON ON THE PLAIN	NO SERMON ON THE MOUNT
BIRTH NARRATIVE	NO BIRTH	BIRTH NARRATIVE	NO BIRTH
CALL OF THE DISCIPLES	CALL OF THE DISCIPLES	NO CALL	NO CALL

Some scholars have tried to harmonize these accounts and explain the differences. Others tend to let them stand on their own.

What about you? Do these differences trip you up or do they help expand your ideas about the Good News?

1

Read the opening lines of Matthew's Gospel and John's Gospel.

- How do these two introductions to Jesus complement one another?

4

The Gospels are filled with the parables Jesus used to help people understand what the Kingdom of God was all about.

- Come up with a modern-day parable that illustrates your sense of the good news.

animate

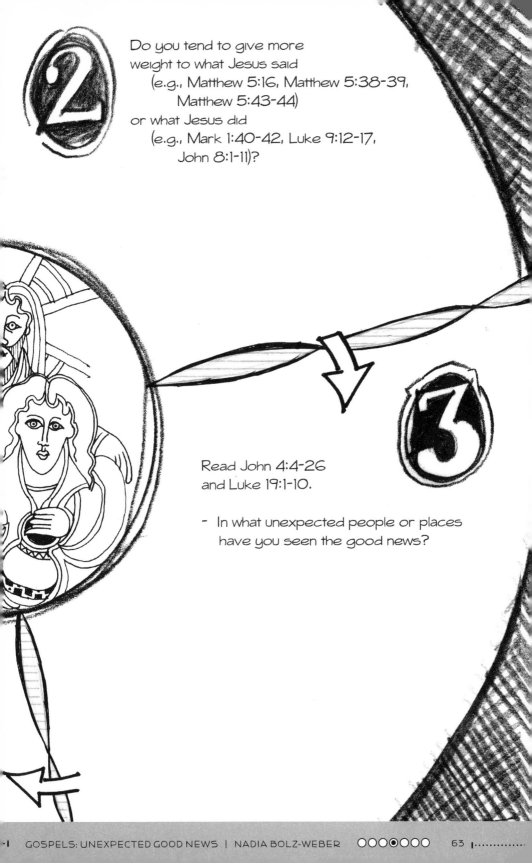

② Do you tend to give more
weight to what Jesus said
  (e.g., Matthew 5:16, Matthew 5:38-39,
     Matthew 5:43-44)
or what Jesus did
  (e.g., Mark 1:40-42, Luke 9:12-17,
     John 8:1-11)?

③

Read John 4:4-26
and Luke 19:1-10.

- In what unexpected people or places
  have you seen the good news?

Signs of good news in
There life

NOTES

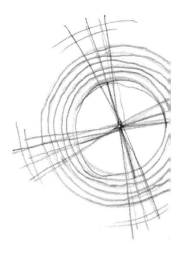

WANT MORE? HERE ARE A FEW SUGGESTIONS
FOR FURTHER READING ON THIS TOPIC.

*Telling the Truth: The Gospel as Tragedy, Comedy, and
Fairy Tale,* Frederick Buechner. HarperOne: 2009.

*Jesus Freak: Feeding, Healing, Raising the
Dead,* Sara Miles. Jossey-Bass, 2010.

Jesus for President: Politics for Ordinary Radicals,
Shane Claiborne and Chris Haw. Zondervan, 2008.

animate ⟨ ....

Notes

animate ⟨

GENRE | RHYTHM OF THE TEXT
JOSÉ MORALES

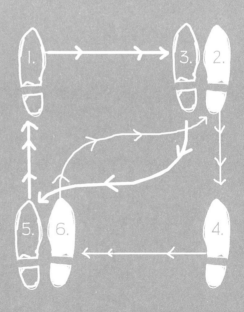

JOSÉ MORALES

Jose Morales is the Executive Regional Minister of the Central Rocky Mountain Region of the Christian Church (Disciples of Christ). He's also a DJ who spins house and tecno music at a club in Denver.

MORE-O-LESS

XTRA II

most of us know how to **DANCE** with the many **genres** of literature. But we don't always extend what we know about genre to our **reading** of the **BIBLE**

Have you had the experience of feeling out of step with the Bible? Like the rhythm is off and you can't seem to get the beat? How do you deal with that?

José points out that we are comfortable with the concept of genre in our music and our literature. So why do we sometimes wrestle with the idea that the Bible is filled with different styles of writing?

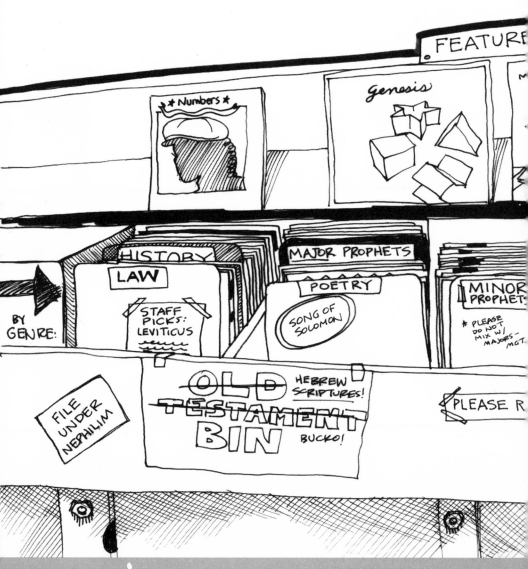

animate

We're naturally drawn to certain types of music. The same is true with the Bible: Which types are you drawn to? Which types do you avoid?

José suggests reading the book of JONAH as a MYTH or ALLEGORY and not as a HISTORICAL EPIC. HOW DOES THAT READING CHANGE THE MEANING of THE BOOK of JONAH FOR YOU?

What do we gain by reading the Bible as a collection of different genres? What do we lose?

How might these ideas about genre change the way you read other books of the Bible?

1

Read the story of the Tower of Babel (Genesis 11:1-9) as history. Now read it again as allegory. How do the implications of this story change when you shift genres?

4

Think of a verse you've heard used in conversation or in an argument. How would thinking about the genre of that passage change the way that verse is understood and used?

2 Read 1 Kings 6:2-10, Psalms 71:14-18, Amos 7:1-9, Revelation 5:1-5. How does your understanding of genre help you make sense of these very different passages?

3 Read Corinthians 6:14-7:1. As with any letter, this one is written to a specific group of people to address a specific situation. What difference does that make in the way you understand Paul's words?

are you ready
new ways

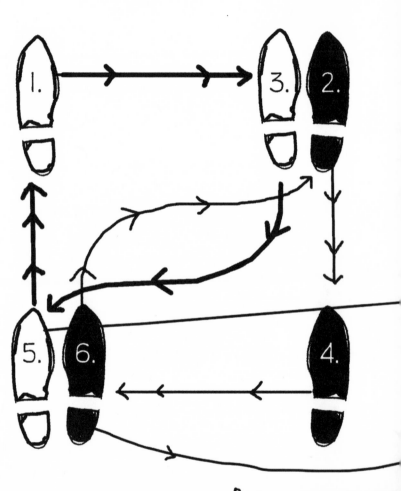

as you learn
you listening

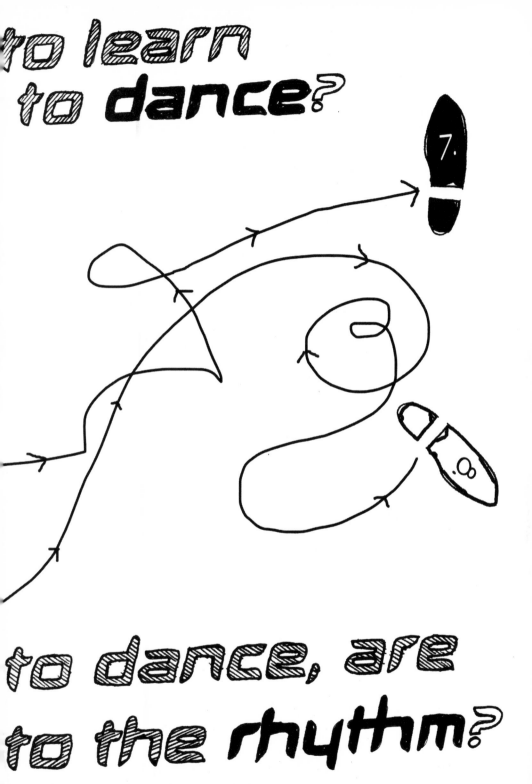

to learn to dance?

to dance, are to the rhythm?

NOTES

WANT MORE? HERE ARE A FEW SUGGESTIONS
FOR FURTHER READING ON THIS TOPIC.

Interpreting the New Testament: A Practical Guide,
Daniel J. Harrington. Liturgical Press, 1990.

How to Read the Bible for All It's Worth, Gordon D.
Fee and Douglas Stuart, Zondervan, 2003.

*Reading the Bible Again For the First Time: Taking
the Bible Seriously But Not Literally,* Marcus
J. Borg. HarperSanFrancisco, 2002.

*Understanding the Bible: An Introduction for
Skeptics, Seekers, and Religious Liberals,*
John Buehrens. Beacon Press, 2004.

Spirituality of the Psalms (Facets Series), Walter
Brueggemann. Fortress Press, 2001.

*Out of the Depths: The Psalms Speak for Us
Today,* Bernhard W. Anderson with Stephen
Bishop. Westminster John Knox Press, 2000.

*An Introduction to the Old Testament: The Canon
and Christian Imagination,* Walter Brueggemann.
Westminster John Knox Press, 2003.

The Writings of the New Testament, Luke
Timothy Johnson. Fortress Press, 2010.

Reading the Bible as Literature, Jeanie C. Crain. Polity, 2010.

*The Good Book: Reading the Bible with Mind and
Heart,* Peter J. Gomes. HarperOne 2002.

NOTES

animate   <

INTERPRETATION | SCRIPTURE READS US
WILL WILLIMON

will WILLIMON

> THE BIBLE IS OFTEN BAFFLINGLY COMPLEX AND MYSTERIOUS.

IT'S WILL WILLIMON!
- Former Bishop of the North Alabama Conference of the United Methodist Church
- Former Dean of Duke Chapel
- Present Professor of the Practice of Christian Ministry at Duke Divinity School
- Author of lots and lots and lots of books, including his latest novel, Incorporation

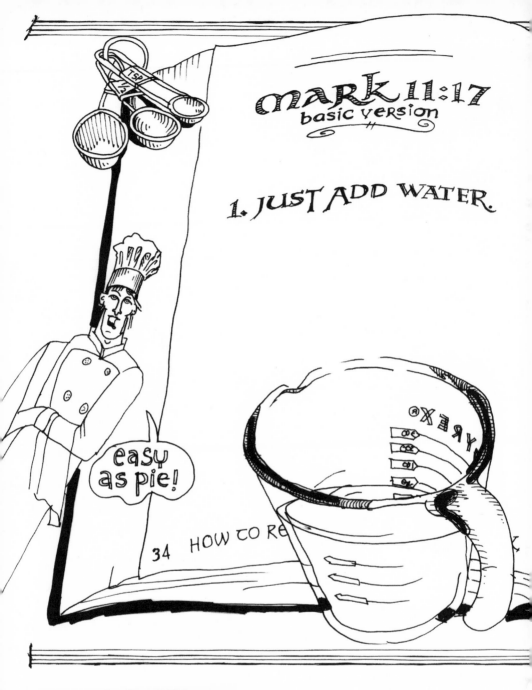

WHY DO WE RESIST THE MORE
COMPLICATED RECIPE FOR
INTERPRETING THE BIBLE?

MARK 11:17
complex version

1. Learn Hebrew, the language of the Hebrew Scriptures.
2. Study Isaiah and recognize the three "Isaiahs" identified by Bible scholars.
3. Study Jeremiah.
4. Study role of prophets in the Ancient Near Eastern world.
5. Study Judaism.
6. Study early church history to determine what Jesus is implying.
7. Learn Aramaic, the language Jesus spoke.
8. Learn Greek, the language in which the Gospels were written.
9. Study the Septuagint, the Greek translation of the Old Testament that was most likely used by the Gospel writers.
10. Read up on daily life in First Century Palestine.
11. Read commentaries on Mark to get a sense of Mark's narrative structure.
12. Compare and contrast the way Mark uses this story with the way Luke tells it in Luke 19:46.
13. Look at this episode without the quote in John 2:14.

Mix, stir well, pray, and let rise indefinitely.

I don't even know where to find this stuff!

How to Read the Bible COOKBOOK 35

WHAT MIGHT WE BE MISSING IF WE STICK WITH THE BASIC RECIPE?

Most of us aren't going to learn Aramaic. So why bother trying to dig deepe
What's the reward for making an effort, as incomplete as it might be?
Will says these efforts stoke, fund, form, and fuel our imaginations.
Which of Will's suggested tools do that for you?

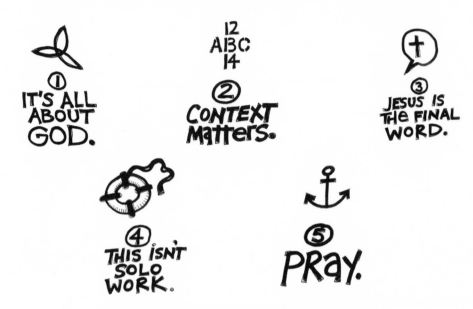

① IT'S ALL ABOUT GOD.

② CONTEXT Matters.

③ JESUS IS THE FINAL WORD.

④ THIS ISN'T SOLO WORK.

⑤ PRay.

How have you seen these various resources fuel your understanding of the Bible?

If you haven't used them, how might they help light a fire in your thoughts about the Bible?

GOD

IMAGINATION STEW

CONTEXT

COMMUNITY

PRAYER

OHIO MATCHES

even if you don't use all the wood in your woodpile, every bit you add will add fuel to the flame.

JESUS

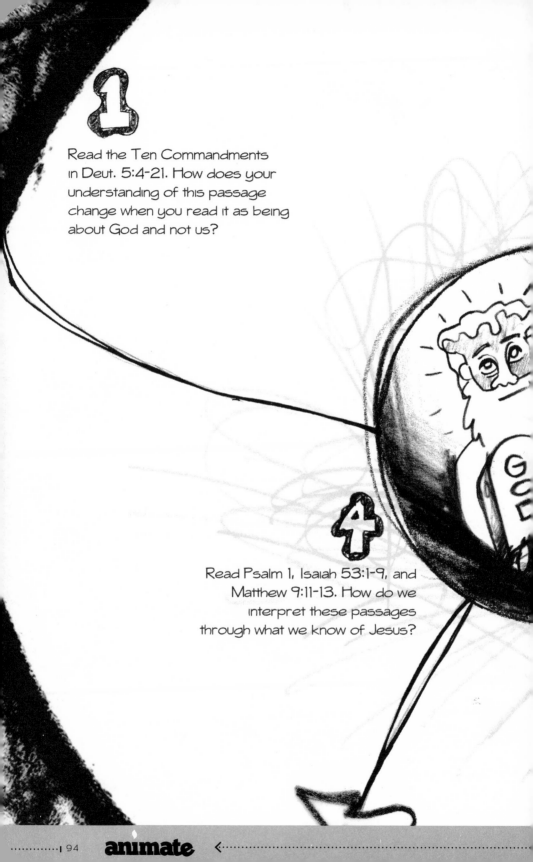

1

Read the Ten Commandments in Deut. 5:4-21. How does your understanding of this passage change when you read it as being about God and not us?

4

Read Psalm 1, Isaiah 53:1-9, and Matthew 9:11-13. How do we interpret these passages through what we know of Jesus?

GOD

2

Read Col. 3:18-4:1.
What information do
you wish you had
about Colossae, the
community reading
this letter, to offer
some context for
this passage?

3

Get in smaller groups
and read Matthew
20:1-16. Give each
person the chance to
talk about what this
passage has to say.

WHAT WOULD IT TAKE FOR THE BIBLE TO BORE INTO YOUR SOUL?

Notes

animate ⟨

WANT MORE? HERE ARE A FEW SUGGESTIONS
FOR FURTHER READING ON THIS TOPIC.

The Art of Reading Scripture, Ellen F. Davis and
Richard B. Hays. Wm. B Eerdmanns, 2003.

Shaped by the Bible, William H. Willimon. Abingdon, 1991.

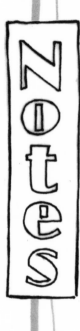

animate ‹...

GRACE | LOVE IS THE BOTTOM LINE

JAY BAKKER

THE NEW TESTAMENT & THE OLD TESTAMENT SET ME FREE.

JAY BAKKER

Jay Bakker is a preacher, speaker, and writer. He has planted churches in Phoenix, Atlanta, NYC, and Minneapolis. In his spare time he makes Batman dioramas.

Jay talks about
the Bible being
used as a weapon,
a fortune cookie,
and a fairy tale.

LEVITICUS 19:28

When has the Bible been used
as a weapon against you or
someone you know?

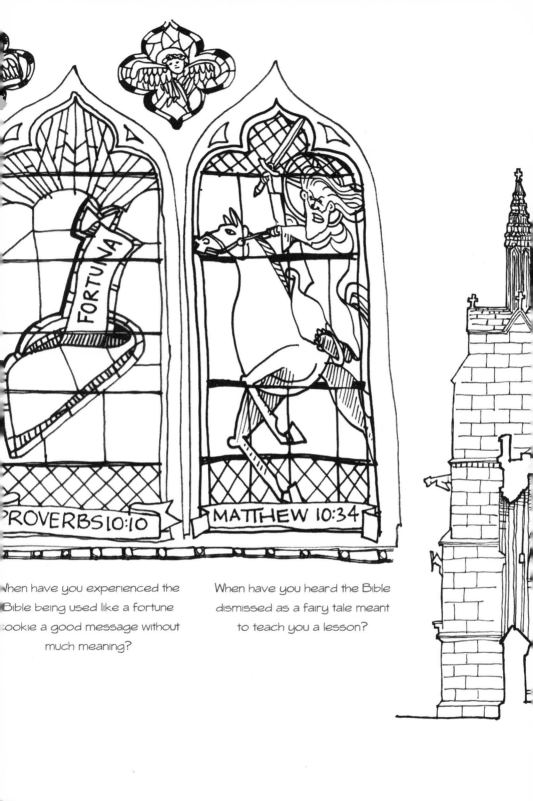

FORTUNA

PROVERBS 10:10

MATTHEW 10:34

When have you experienced the Bible being used like a fortune cookie a good message without much meaning?

When have you heard the Bible dismissed as a fairy tale meant to teach you a lesson?

Jay admits to having a difficult history with the Bible. His turning point came when he broke through the messages he'd heard and looked into the Bible for himself.

We have a choice to make as well. We can look away or break through to a more honest relationship with the Bible. Which are you more inclined to do? Why?

animate

1

Read Mark 7:25-30

Jesus doesn't always act in a way that we might see as loving or kind. What do you make of that?

4

Read 1 Cor. 13

This chapter is often called the "Love Chapter," but what if there's more here than a simple call to be loving? What does Christian love really look like?

Read Galatians 3:26-29
How do Paul's words help us reconsider
the social, political, and theological
boundaries we deal with today?

2

Read Deut. 20:1-20
This is one of those passages that can make us
want to turn away from the Bible. How could Jay's
suggestion of using a Jesus lens and a Paul lens
help us make more sense of stories like this?

3

"SOMETIMES I WANT TO WALK AWAY FROM MY FAITH BECAUSE OF THE BIBLE. —

> BUT THE IDEA OF LOVING MY ENEMIES AS MYSELF, THE IDEA OF GRACE, DRAWS ME BACK "
> —J.B.

What's keeping you from reading this book?

NOTES

WANT MORE? HERE ARE A FEW SUGGESTIONS
FOR FURTHER READING ON THIS TOPIC.

Doubts and Loves, Richard Holloway. Canongate UK, 2005.

The Shaking of the Foundations, Paul Tillich
(especially the chapter "Accept That You
Are Accepted"). Wipf   Stock, 2012.

The New Christians: Dispatches from the Emergent
Frontier, Tony Jones. Jossey-Bass, 2009.

notes

animate

NOTES

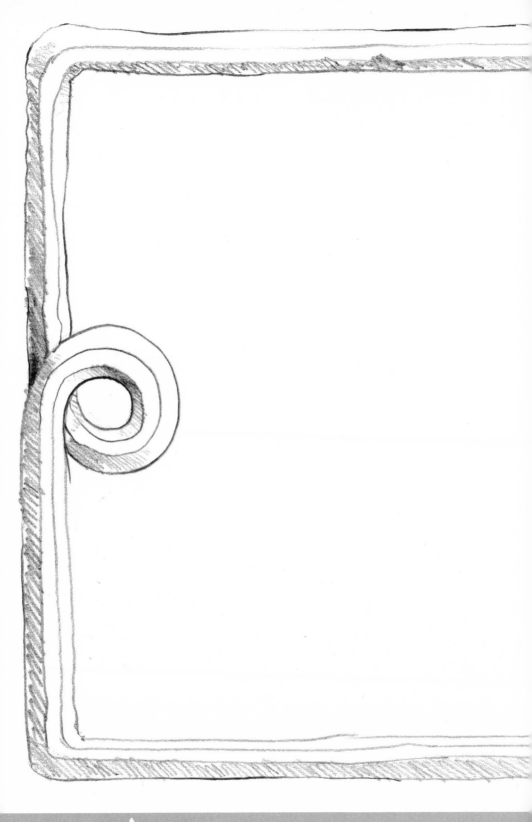

animate ‹

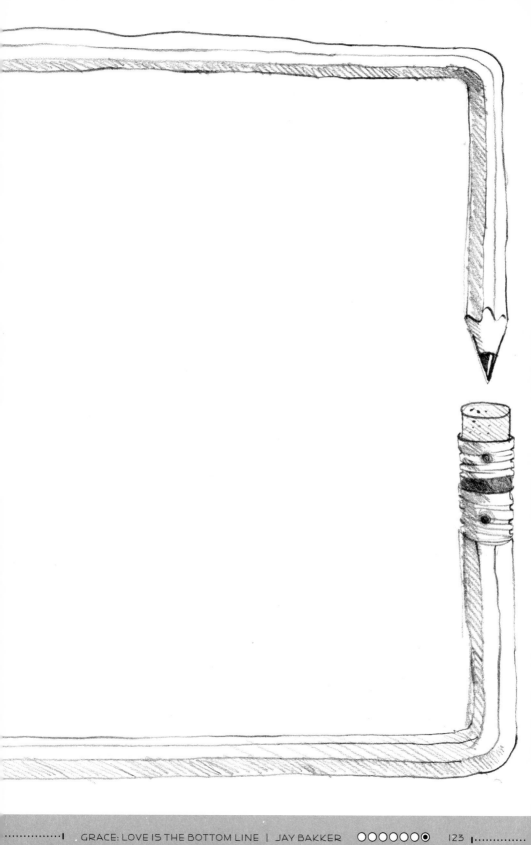

animate

ISBN 978-1-4514-7288-2

51499